Other books in the series:
The Crazy World of Birdwatching (Peter Rigby)
The Crazy World of Cats (Bill Stott)
The Crazy World of Cricket (Bill Stott)
The Crazy World of Gardening (Bill Stott)
The Crazy World of Golf (Mike Scott)
The Crazy World of the Handyman (Roland Fiddy)
The Crazy World of Hospitals (Bill Stott)
The Crazy World of Jogging (David Pye)
The Crazy World of Love (Roland Fiddy)
The Crazy World of Marriage (Bill Stott)
The Crazy World of Music (Bill Stott)
The Crazy World of the Office (Bill Stott)
The Crazy World of Photography (Bill Stott)
The Crazy World of the Royals (Barry Knowles)
The Crazy World of Rugby (Bill Stott)
The Crazy World of Sailing (Peter Rigby)
The Crazy World of Sex (David Pye)
The Crazy World of Skiing (Craig Peterson & Jerry Emerson)
The Crazy World of Tennis (Peter Rigby)

Published in Great Britain in 1991 by
Exley Publications Ltd, 16 Chalk Hill,
Watford, Herts WD1 4BN, United Kingdom.

ISBN 1-85015-276-4

Printed and bound in Spain

the CRAZY world of SCHOOL

Cartoons by Bill Stott

EXLEY

"My mother says I'm her little angel, were you ever a little angel, Mr. Sidebottom?"

"*I wonder what you have to do wrong to grow up like Mr. Trimblett?*"

"I'm having parental trauma. They'd like me to go into medicine. I want to be a bimbo."

"Come on Doris, you have to see the funny side ..."

"Yes, we find her difficult to control, too ..."

"He tells me to fasten my tie properly – and look at the state of him!"

"*Jason lacks concentration Mr. Fittock ... MR. FITTOCK!*"

"The foreign legion regret that they have no vacancies just now."

"We always knew putting Mr. Warburton with 3B was a gamble ..."

"So do I, Gary, so do I."

"Hold it Miss Bainbridge – I think the ass wants to wee."

"If he's got a first class degree, I don't think I want one."

"Idle, insolent, shiftless? Did I write that? Well, well ..."

"The trouble with educational jokes is that you might end up working for them ..."

"Oh, and you've got Melainie Bainbridge out here exercising her right as a sun worshipper not to go to assembly."

"It's amazing! I told him my homework would be late because a volcano erupted under our house ... and he believed me!"

"While Kirsty may have torched your lab – may I remind you
that her father is head of the P.T.A.?"

"Mr. Hardisty's letting 3B get to him ..."

"'Course teachers lie – read that!"

"Wouldn't it be great if, just once, nurse discovered somebody with a really horrible disease?"

"Sex education with 3B is quite an experience, eh Miss Wellbeloved?"

"The new teacher's got a confidence problem."

"*But Sharon – bright red zits with big yellow heads right on the end of your nose are all part of life's rich tapestry.*"

"Why did I opt to do art? Simple. They wouldn't have me in music, drama, chemistry, French, biology, technology or history."

"Miss! Miss! Melody Hargreaves has thrown up on Henry
the hamster!"

"I've bought an executive-style briefcase, had my hair re-vamped, grown a fashionable moustache – and the little beasts still throw things at me ..."

"I want to be sure you love me for my mind as well as my body ..."

"'Morning Debbie – which one of your fan-club did your homework this week?"

"I'm looking for the chewing gum you made me throw away last Monday ..."

"Please sir, Catriona Everard is telling tales again!"

"Correction Mrs. Harmsworth, Terence doesn't 'play' truant –
he's dead serious about it!"

"Rules or no rules Flanagan, I've a good mind to box your ears ..."

"And if NASA have no vacancies – what then?"

"Mr. Fittock's nostrils are even hairier than my grandad's!"

"Sir? How do you draw cleavages?"

"It was just bad luck sir. <u>Anybody</u> could make a bad smell during assembly!"

"The lad's a trier – he started that coffee table in the first year."

"*I'm afraid the lunch hour art club will have to disband –
Louise McFadden is offering life poses to anybody who'll do
her homework.*"

"So far, Headmaster, we've had 397 calls claiming responsibility ..."

"I suppose one of the hidden bonuses of sports day is seeing the Head in his tracksuit."

"I'm just not the swimming type sir. Sometimes I throw up in the bath!"

*"Geoffrey Wilson won't tell me what French kissing is, Miss....
What's French kissing Miss?"*

"You certainly know where you stand with this new Head..."

"Threatening me with your father is useless Tomkinson. I have it on good authority that like you, he is a wimp."

"... and that's our Mr. Whiteside. In theory, a brilliant chemistry teacher. In practice ..."

"*Dad sent a note Miss ...*"

"Just another reason why I hate gym."

"Leave him alone. Only an idiot tries to keep 3B in detention
on the last day of term …"

"I'm warning you 3B. I have a B.A., an M.A., and a Ph.D. and I _will_ find out who made that awful smell!"

"Well, the Head will need hospitalizing, but it is a new record."

"We'd like her on our team – her game's fairly average, but she swears better than John McEnroe!"

"Cute! She said you were cute!"

"Aw come on – my dad told me about it – you go behind the bike sheds and it all happens!"

"What's this secret project I've been hearing about?"

"It must be fantastic to be in the last year – imagine being able to go to the toilet without asking!"

"What we have here, Headmistress, is the logical extension of the 'my dad can beat your dad up' syndrome ..."

"You ask me why I get such a lot of time off? There go three good reasons."

"Somewhere along the line we're going wrong – according to Fiona Pratt tadpoles come from frogs bonking."

"I have no doubt that you would like to be a mercenary when you leave, Clinton, but it's going to help if you spell it correctly on the application form ..."

"We all get pimples from time to time Joanne – now take your head out of the desk, there's a good girl ..."

"Cheating? No sir. I just happened to sit behind someone with the answers written on the back of his white sweater sir."

"Why am I in detention? Because when Mrs. Lovejoy asked if there were any questions, I asked her why she always asked if there were any questions when there never were ..."

"Once many years ago, I held a class spellbound ..."

"So it's true about Mr. Leapwell leaving teaching?"

"He's a hero in our class. Miss Parkinson accused him of acting like Rambo."

"*This apple is not just a gift, Miss. The fact is – I love you.*"

Books from the "Crazy World" series:

The Crazy World of Birdwatching. £3.99. By Peter Rigby. Over seventy cartoons on the strange antics of the twitcher brigade. One of our most popular pastimes, this will be a natural gift for any birdwatcher.

The Crazy World of Cats. £3.99. By Bill Stott. Fat cats, alley cats, lazy cats, sneaky cats – from the common moggie to the pedigree Persian – you'll find them all in this witty collection. If you've ever wondered what your cat was really up to, this is for you.

The Crazy World of Cricket. £3.99. By Bill Stott. This must be Bill Stott's silliest cartoon collection. It makes an affectionate present for any cricketer who can laugh at himself.

The Crazy World of Gardening. £3.99. By Bill Stott. The perfect present for anyone who has ever wrestled with a lawnmower that won't start, over-watered a pot plant or been assaulted by a rose bush from behind.

The Crazy World of Golf. £3.99. By Mike Scott. Over seventy hilarious cartoons show the fanatic golfer in his (or her) every absurdity. What really goes on out on the course, and the golfer's life when not playing are chronicled in loving detail.

The Crazy World of the Handyman. £3.99. By Roland Fiddy. This book is a must for anyone who has ever hung *one* length of wallpaper upside down or drilled through an electric cable. A gift for anyone who has ever tried to "do it yourself" and failed!

The Crazy World of Hospitals. £3.99. By Bill Stott. Hilarious cartoons about life in a hospital. A perfect present for a doctor or a nurse – or a patient who needs a bit of fun.

The Crazy World of Love. £3.99. By Roland Fiddy. This funny yet tender collection covers every aspect of love from its first joys to its dying embers. An ideal gift for lovers of all ages to share with each other.

The Crazy World of Marriage. £3.99. By Bill Stott. The battle of the sexes in close-up from the altar to the grave, in public and in private, in and out of bed. See your friends, your enemies (and possibly yourselves?) as never before!

The Crazy World of the Office. £3.99. By Bill Stott. Laugh your way through the office jungle with Bill Stott as he observes the idiosyncrasies of bosses, the deviousness of underlings and the goings-on at the Christmas party.... A must for anyone who has ever worked in an office!

The Crazy World of Photography. £3.99. By Bill Stott. Everyone who owns a camera, be it a Box Brownie or the latest Pentax, will find something to laugh at in this superb collection. The absurdities of the camera freak will delight your whole family.

The Crazy World of the Royals. £3.99. By Barry Knowles. In over seventy hilarious cartoons Barry Knowles captures the funny side of Britain's greatest institution! A real treat for royal watchers everywhere.

The Crazy World of Rugby. £3.99. By Bill Stott. From schoolboy to top international player, no-one who plays or watches rugby will escape Bill Stott's merciless exposé of their habits and absurdities. Over seventy hilarious cartoons – a must for addicts.

The Crazy World of Sex. £3.99. By David Pye. A light-hearted look at the absurdities and weaker moments of human passion – the turn-ons and the turn-offs. Very funny and in (reasonably) good taste.

The Crazy World of Skiing. £3.99. By Craig Peterson and Jerry Emerson. Covering almost every possible (and impossible) experience on the slopes, this is an ideal present for anyone who has ever strapped on skis – and instantly fallen over.

The Crazy World of Tennis. £3.99. By Peter Rigby. Would-be Stephen Edbergs and Steffi Grafs watch out! This brilliant collection will pin-point their pretensions and poses. Whether you play by yourself or only watch TV, this will amuse and entertain you!

These books make super presents. Order them from your local bookseller or from Exley Publications Ltd, Dept BP, 16 Chalk Hill, Watford, Herts WD1 4BN. (Please send £1.50 for one book or £2.25 for two or more to cover postage and packing.)